G000230777

Kite Envy

I want to be free

Sang Ji

Published by Opera on Sarovar Press

First published in Great Britain
by Opera on Sarovar Press 2015

www.sangsnotebook.com

A catalogue record for this book is available from the
British Library

ISBN 978-0-9934536-0-1

Printed and bound by CPI Group (UK) Ltd
Croydon, CR0 4YY

Published by Opera on Sarovar Press

*I would like to thank my parents
for encouraging my creativity*

This book is dedicated to:

All,

Birds and Kites
Who wish
To Fly
But don't know how,
It's okay
There is a way,
And Know
You are not Alone
In a Desire to grow
Wings of Your own
Design.

Prologue

Beginnings are constantly appearing in our lives.
Opportunities to live more truly and fully bump
into us throughout our day, but we don't always
recognise them.

I would say that a beginning is anything that causes
you to change your rhythm –
the beat of your heart
the pace of your breath
a rush of nerves as your face turns towards or away;
when you hesitate, pause or smile,
as your ears prick up or a laugh falls out
as you get a paper cut, or drop a dollar;
it is a moment before you cry,
the decision (conscious or not) to let anger reign
and it is the calm afterwards.

Anything and everything can be a new beginning.

Perhaps we tend to take more notice when the
beginning that we find ourselves in happens to be
in the middle of a mess. In that moment we have
to believe that beginnings are blessings in disguise.
And we have to reach, with courage, beyond that
beginning to know this.

From then on, the beginning seems inevitable; more
necessary and beautiful than it ever felt or seemed
in the moment of that beginning. Realising this,
we trust that every cloud has a rainbow within it
waiting to be birthed.

In an interview between Oprah Winfrey and Maya Angelou in May 2013, Oprah recounts a moment in her past, where she found herself on her knees and crying. Still on her knees and crying she picks up the phone and calls Maya, who tells her:

> "Stop [crying] right now.
> I want you to say, Thank You".

When Oprah asks what she should be saying thank you for, Maya replies:

> "Because you know God has put
> a rainbow in the clouds for you."

So I can afford to smile and relax a little in the face of now. Any now. Because glancing back, Now will be either a beautiful memory or a sacred moment that changed the way I pursued the rest.

Sang Ji
England
2015

Kite Envy

I want to be free

Regents Park
Walking one summer's afternoon

He looks so ... peaceful
The opposite of me

We are standing so close
He does not even notice
He is too busy
Flying
With his Kite

I wonder what it feels like
To fly
I wonder what his hands perceive
Connected
To that
Motion

I stop and sit and watch, headphones in.

I do not know how long I sit for. I cannot take my
eyes away from his face; it is more mesmerising than
the Kite itself, blowing in its colourful eminence.

Restless

*About an hour ago I was overcome with a deep
restlessness radiating from the innermost part
of my body. I couldn't control it and no matter
what I did or said to myself it remained: this
feeling of being unsatisfied – with everything*

I am not at work
today. I have the day
off and all to myself.
And during this
day-off nothingness,
it surfaces – a gentle
and constant nudge –
and it happens
somewhere in the
region between my
stomach and my neck.
After a while of being
subjected to the gentle
and constant nudge,
I feel pressured to do
something; not any
kind of something,
something Productive.

I fight against it –
It is my Day Off!
A day purposefully
taken to *not* work, to
abstain my
consciousness from
any kind of to-do list.

How many times
have I sat at my desk,
fantasising about lazy
mornings that stretch
into the evening and
the only thing to do is
relax; smiling as
I watch myself take
turns to 'chill' at a
pool on my inflatable
lillo or sprawling on a
sun-lounger gobbling
up some Saul Williams
(or a verse or two
of Maya Angelou)?

Yet a voice insists
about all the things
I should be doing, so
many tiny elbows keep
nudging in that gentle
and constant manner
that I cannot ignore.

I give in. I pay
attention to the voice.

It supplies me with
a list of one hundred
and one things I could
do right now, none of
which I particularly
fancy doing.

And then it tells
me that I am wasting
Time (and I hate the
idea of wasting Time).

Another voice, steeped
in a neck-cracking
eyeball-rolling attitude
interrupts:
'What do you want to be
doing then?'
I almost beg myself
pardon, but there
isn't time –
'C'mon, right now, in
this very minute, what
do you want?!?'

I don't have an
answer.

Then I realise
that I don't have
an answer.
And that's when
I start to freak out.

Amongst the
commotion inside

yet another voice
quieter than the first
two, observes that the
question being posed
is probably the easiest
question in the world.
It continues, slightly
exasperated, asking
how could I not know
what I would like to
do right now!

My heart expands into
my head where it
throbs desperately,
sending ripples
through my ears down
my neck into my chest,
disrupting the flow
of breath.

Unnerved, I search
myself for a response.
A thousand possible
'answers' stumble
across my mind; I feel
my body tighten
because none of them
are right – and then
I go blank – and pause
– and then – the voices
demand in chorus:

Don't you even
know yourself?

An Aside

That was the moment when I became conscious of a
Me within myself.

Many more Me's perhaps; that I may be more than
I perceived myself to be up to this point in my life;
that perhaps there were other parts of me that lived
inside. How else could I explain voices that were not
mine but sounded like me? That spoke without
consciously articulating?

That question, asking whether I even knew myself,
provoked the beginning of a deeply personal journey.
A search had begun, only I did not know what I was
searching for – I did not even know who started the
search. It became a journey within a journey.

And it was disorientating; often it felt that no one
could relate. I struggled to express my responses to
what life was throwing at me; things that none of my
peers seemed to be experiencing. I didn't ask
around, and lacked courage to confide in anyone,
because it wasn't the kind of stuff people talked
about. But I needed to understand what was going
on inside of me. So I began to write out the
conversations that I was not having, unsure where
I was going with it, or whether it would help.

Meanwhile, daily life continued in the same rhythm:
I would wake up on Monday morning at six(ish),
speed through my morning routine to catch the
07:26 or 07:56 train to work. Get to work and work.
Leave work, exhale and catch two trains home,
hoping for no delays. Reach home. Have an

evening, which looked something like: eat, chit chat, dodge thoughts, help with homework or housework, wonder as I did these things if there was anything more I could be, read a little, sometimes write if I felt like it. The best part was taking a long shower and then jumping into bed (occasionally treating myself to a bedside hot chocolate). Sleep. Wake. Repeat until the weekend. Weekends were weekends, spent doing standard weekend things: socialising, tidying up, a bit of yoga, family time, shopping, lazing around, eating, relaxing ... mulling over what next, perhaps adding a couple of bricks to my castles in the sky. By Sunday evening the Monday blues would kick in, and then five days would pass by so fast – over – and over.

I didn't have time to stop and confront that restless feeling. But it persisted. Every single day I felt it lingering in the in-between moments – the pause between opening my eyes and turning off the alarm, as I boarded the train, whilst waiting for the kettle to boil ...

Soon the restlessness formed itself into letters and spaces and question marks.
They started innocently enough:
Am I sure this is the right job for me? Do I want to be partner in the firm when they don't even look happy? Do I want the same thing as them?
Then they became slightly more probing:
Do I fit in here? Am I making a difference? Why don't we see things the same way?
The direction changed:
What am I doing? Who am I? Why am I here?
And I often arrived simply and indiscriminately at:
Why?

In my mind I would fast-forward to my future, but I couldn't quite see it. Something was missing from the picture, and I felt scared because I did not know what it was. Imagination failed me because I did not know what I wanted.

When I finally dared to share some of these questions with others I received responses that lacked truthful vibration – they weren't lying; but absent was the conviction of having lived through those questions. How could they have reached the answers they were providing me with if they had lived only one version of life? Still, I listened and took what they gave me. But I wasn't satisfied simply because the restlessness was still there. Eventually I stopped asking and I looked those questions in the eye.

The answers did not come straight away or in the way I expected them to – in flashes of insight or as flowing, coherent prose. They came in Random Moments, unexpectedly. As soon as I became aware of this, I would grab hold of those moments and their lessons, and capture them in my notebook. That was the only place I could make sense of them. I was sure that together, these reflections could, would, must make a Whole. These Precious Moments, some so-here-and-now and others so subtle I had to hold my breath and shut my eyes to experience them, formed the basis of my own self-illumination and a new happiness.

By paying attention to these seemingly insignificant Moments I started to piece together my answers to what I was seeking: Freedom.

To Fly:
I fell into the well of "I",
To know myself
I unearthed many selves
Until I reached
Sacred waters.
The result:
An opus from my heart,
Etched onto water
Reflected onto paper
Sewn into the wings of kite.
This is Kite Envy.

Step One

Putting pen to paper was uncomfortable.
I did not know how or where to start
I was unsure about what was coming out.

It *did* feel like I was taking some responsibility
for this thing called life – that was apparently
mine, though I could not say if I owned it.
On paper, though, I had the space to have a say.

Work out the direction the wind is travelling in.
Then stand with your back to the wind, and hold
your kite out in front of you.

Pen, Me, Paper

Write something
Anything
Something
Anything
Something
Anything
Something
Anything
Something
Anything

I wish
I knew what it is that I want to know.

Sitting in Bed

Everyone should have a room called My Room

It's late. Been a long day.
Just want to close my eyes
– I think, in part, to suppress Thought.

Fear tugs at my eyelids,
I breathe shallow in its presence. Tired,
yet I find myself reaching towards my desk
past the softly lit lamp, fingers stretch for my notepad
and any pen. I want to write down all the things I *do*
know and *can* be sure about – cement convictions –
in case doubt creeps in later.

I'm grateful for a quiet room, dark, apart from a lazy
bedside spotlight that shines on me highlighting my
existence – and nothing else. There is no one and
nothing to think about, because they are somewhere
in the darkness.

I think about reading a book, but decide against it;
I tell myself *no distractions*. Sometimes it's fine just to
be – to feel my body heavy against sheets that tighten
and draw taut under my tired person.
I am supported by linen.
Comforted by cotton.
Let the world pass around me while
I am still.

Here I am – part of the world – yet not particularly
involved. Like a bird perched on electricity cables
that hang across field and road.

Music reaches me from my sister's bedroom.

Voices gabbling downstairs
are muffled by the floorboards.
Chitter-chatter passes by outside my window
Tyres meet speed bumps in syncopated slap

Between these sounds and my ears
there is a buffer of space: My Room.

The air is still.
It respectfully surrounds me and reminds me of
Who I am.
I look at all the stuff decorating my room:
clothes spilling off the back of a chair
piles of books and notebooks
mugs
assortments of pens and clips (which I can never find
when I need them)
shoes and handbags.

Walls plastered in little notes with scraps of the
World I hope to see one day.

It is a comfort to be here, in My Room.
I don't want anyone and yet I seek everyone's Love –
for them to love me the way I want them to.
But to do so I'd have to change them all.
And because I can't change them (I only recently got
the message that people won't change unless they
want to) I sit here in my own world and just Be.
And Breathe.
And not consciously think;
let thoughts take shape *I keep thinking about this person*

I am falling asleep;
but my hand wants to write –
like it's trying to push something out.

Big Fight - Same Issues
Because love doesn't guarantee understanding.
And love isn't always humble.
Love isn't always relevant

Yesterday we argued. Your misunderstanding of me
– almost – isolated me.

      I know that you love me.

That sense of aloneness became a sense of oneness;
drove me into the arms of myself for comfort.

      I know that you love me.

Either they are right and I am wrong – in which case
I should apologise and continue as normal – but
I can't – what I said felt right.

      I have to decide: me or them.

I have to decide because I'm done trying to explain,
justify, rationalise. They just don't get it - they don't
see. They wear toughened glass spectacles.
They can deal with the shouting but not the crying;
that's where I lose them.

      I know that you love me.

      I don't know where to go from here.

I don't Love what I see
I want to laugh but I hold it in, muffle it

A handful of years ago
I remember laughing out loud
For REAL
A proper Sang-laugh!
The experience was freeing
I fell in love with me
With the sound of me;
Laughter consumed me
I became pure expression.
Did I say I fell in love with me?

After that
I repeatedly experienced an
Overwhelming sense of chasing
But not reaching;
I began to realise that
I did not love
What I was seeing around me.

There are good things.
But I want to love my life.
I want to laugh *that laugh* – everyday!

What does that mean for me?

I want to be able to sit on this
Seven-minute-tube-ride
Without a to-do-list;
Enjoy whatever is before me
As we zoom at an average of
33 kilometres per hour between
Old Street and London Bridge.

A Moment of Peace
in a Blueberry Muffin

Being in the moment, present to myself

As I walk, I squeeze
the crinkled shiny
foil gently using the
whole of my hand;
four fingers and a
thumb make sure
that every inch of
skin enjoys the slow
impression into it of
the metallic wrapper,
from the blueberry
delight that I ingested
minutes before.

The wrapper is now
small enough to fit
inside the front pocket
of my bag. I lick my
lips the whole time.
That was a good
blueberry muffin.

I close my eyes as
my tongue searches
crevices of my mouth,
behind back teeth and
gums where wisdom
teeth haven't grown
through yet, between
tough molars, sliding

along soft lubricated
cheek walls, for traces
of crumbs from the
sponge, or skin of the
blueberries caught
from the cake. A
thoroughly enjoyable
forensic investigation.

I locate a small bit of
cake behind a tooth
farthest back, softened
by warm saliva.

As I suck it out of the
tooth's grip I retreat
further under the hood
of my puffer jacket
until my vision is
decorated by the fur
lining that runs along
the edge of the hood.

I keep walking.

Sounds are rough and
muffled and my mind
disconnects a little, like
pulling a plug partway
out of the mains.

"You can see me, but that's about it" is my mantra from under the hood.

If I happen to make eye contact with a passer-by I might offer an uncommitted smile. I would rather not be noticed.

Is there ever only silence?

In the safety of disconnection
I shrug off caring what people around me are doing
saying
thinking.

Instead I turn my focus inwards: Thoughts.

Some evaporate into the air around me. Others, immature or not ready to leave or bound to memories, bounce back and collide – like fluffy bumper-cars, creating confusion, roadblocks, and mental traffic.

After some time I don my traffic warden uniform and jump into my head; sort out what's going on inside, so that I can walk through my front door ready for the weekend.

Expression
I want to tell you something about me

I never do of course.

I just want to *express myself* without holding back
because I am worried that you will think differently
of me.

I share only those parts of me that I think you want
to see. I share what I feel comfortable with, knowing
that it will be accepted (hopefully).

Of course it's not *great* to accessorise with fears and
insecurities; but surely it is equally unhealthy to only
show the world your brave face. Why protect
yourself from a beautiful sky and chirping birds, the
warmth of another? Perhaps it is not a conscious act.

Sometimes I am not even *aware* that I am hurting.
Yet I am certain enough to put it in writing: that hurt
shows up in various forms throughout our days and
even as we sleep.

Moments are revealing. I did not know I had it in
me until it came out; and neither did they – it was
a surprise to us all. I know *now*, though, that all it
means is that I am human. I am human, too.
I hurt too. And I want to be loved (too).

I believe that we do not spend enough time *allowing* ourselves to hurt. To feel, to sit it out. We force happiness (and a lot of the time it works until we get That Feeling – then we reach for the remote control or Facebook or a version of Nestlé's sugary distractions).

I fight sadness when it comes.
I resist anger when it rises.
Which is silly. Because if it *is there*, then it *will* reappear.

So why can't I just say it?

Three Minute Soul Mate

I ... I'm not. Can't.
Don't want to exist.
Can't cope with it
all – I ... I ... don't have
an answer.
I'm hedged in, in this
black hole, a gap
between consciousness
and reason – just
intense emotion – –
I_ am_ fear_
sadness_confusion.
I can't feel myself;
yet that's all I feel.
Me and cold. Detached
from the world –
numb. Hear black.
Brain not processing.

Alone.

...

They're all home now
– hear car doors shut:
slam – slam –
slamslam. Need to
snap out of it – but
I'm overwhelmed.
Keys fiddle in the lock,
rush of feet shuffle on
wood, plastic bags
rustle. I carry my
nothingness, lift my

emotions, like cradling
a 14-pound baby in a
diaper made for
Chinese new-borns,
and walk to the
kitchen. And try to
act normal – start
unpacking edibles,
putting carrots in the
fridge and bread by
the toaster – but it's
eating a hole in my
stomach.

I stop after two bags to
place numb hands on
the silent wordless
screaming. I can't
concentrate on the
conversation. I'm not
really here. So I leave;
go upstairs to take a
hot shower. To Soothe
... My Restless Soul.

Upstairs, walking past
the study doors, I feel
it before I hear it –
shoulders gently drop
and a fizz diffuses my
body as if stepping
into sunshine in the
middle of the night.

A sweet-tempered
shock vibrates to and
through my fibres to
the tip of my skin.
Jumping synapses.
Then I hear it. And
they jump some more.

Music.
Shatters the dissonance
into smaller
manageable pieces.

Music.
Notes dodge resistance
and seep deep into my
pores – blind the
senses into momentary
peace – taking me
away from myself.

Melody speaks:
I understand you
Music invites: *Let me
take you away – for a
slice of eternity*

Sounds support my
Inner, props her up for
three or four minutes.
And rejuvenates. And
you know that you are
not the only one.

Music circles arms
around my heart and

gags the mind. Then
loosens the clutch
around my stomach.

Music.
Takes you away – not
far – but far enough.

Music: three minute
soul mate, best friend;
yet unlike any I've
had.

I shut myself in the
study letting song after
song fill up the air
particles around me,
finding their way into
me eventually; charge
the electrons around
me and then me.

I don't know how it
does it; I don't know
why the words hit me
differently to the same
words spoken from
concerned tones.

*Invisible
Lips
Soothe.
Don't need to see you
Music
You come from a
different place.*

I'm kinda lost
as to what I can do

I'm kinda lost as to what I can *do*.
I shy away from prayer 'cos I've got so much to lose –
It's hard to form words without fear or resenting
I don't mean to
      So I berate myself for having such feelings
All the while muttering the next line of prayer:
I'm so sorry
Turn the page
And continue recounting His virtues.

I just want to let it out.
To cry and cry and tell the world that it's been the
hardest few years – but they won't ever know –
I see the way they look at me, though, as if they do.

How do I want the world to see me?
Sometimes I don't.
If they don't see the truth
Then what is the point in looking my way at all?
I say this, yet still try to impress them;
I continue to aspire to meet expectations,
I supply selected facts, imply the truth
Hoping they'll fill in the gaps in my favour.

But – and here's the thing
Even *if* they knew
They would probably have something to say about it,
So it doesn't really make a difference does it?
You, me
We all are what they want us to be in their heads –

the cause, reason, blame, scapegoat, possibility,
obstacle, distraction, hope, responsibility, priority
(the list endless and subjective).
And I guess that's fine, harmless –
As long as *I* know that and don't buy into their
Version of me as well.

That's why sometimes it's easier
To take refuge in a pen, a piano, a song.
I can't explain – but it helps –
When someone isn't there – it just helps.

Even though I do not always come to an answer
And the situation does not change
I arrive at a place I call 'enough',
I am restored, loved even.
I do not know how.

I can't start Writing yet
On the 07:56 train to work

I can't start writing yet
Outside is too beautiful!
Autumn parades her pageant face –
Cool, aloof, misty;
And spotlight rays drench
Everything
Exposing her tenderness.

Ah! See those geese
Reclining on endless thrones
Of long brown grass;
Such a gaggle I've not seen –
Unless on river banks
Or shores
– it makes the turf look cosy.

I don't fear Winter
Or her cold
When Autumn's mornings are so peaceful
And unapologetically individual.
I doubt she's anyone's favourite season,
Yet there's a freshness about her
Which uplifts,
And makes me feel like
Turning anew myself.

Desires unmet

*Rumi said: 'Respond to every call of
your spirit'. I did not understand it then*

Desires – unmet – create lines on faces.

Desires – unheard – pull on heartstrings.
The human recognises this as yearning.

Desires – unmet – generate pretence, detectable in
a lustreless response to life's most telling question:
'How are things with you?'
               What can you say when you are
desperately lagging behind life's aspirations?

Desires – unmet – resound in an ubiquitous pang the
moment you spot what you yearn for nestled in the
arms of another; many a time I found myself there:
standing by watching, longing to share for a moment.

Desires – unheard – compose boring days that leave
me feeling like I have less than I do. The world
seems devoid of stimulation once you ignore yourself
for long enough. True sensations become a nuisance.

Today I walk in leaden shoes; nothing can lift me.
Part of me does not *want* to be lifted; it just craves
a safe place to unfold. I think I am developing an
appetite for My Desires: To Live Them, *Become* Them.

And if I am not yet there, nowhere near,
When I cannot explain all this in response to life's
most telling question because it cannot fit into a four
second window you give me to answer,
Then just let me Breathe.

How to be "Happy"

Slap a smile onto my face – it's easy:
command cheeks to move in horizontally
opposing directions (simple physics really)

But those who love me can tell.

And it's the worst feeling to lie when you know
that they know that you are not letting them in.
Keeping them out.

I understand how it can feel like an insult,
That I don't trust you – but it is just not that.
The on-goings within have not yet formed
into words.

Also,
I am still sailing on the promise of happiness; and
unhappiness is such a useless, weightless confession.
Like damp.
It would leave us both helpless
Unless I have an idea of where my treasure is buried.

So give me some time.
And in the meantime, just go along with the smile.
It means I am trying.
It means I am trying.
It means I have not given up hope.

Bike Ride!

I took a bath and came downstairs.
Everyone was Sat Around; nothing was happening –
it was a limbo moment, that mediocre pause between
dinner being ready and being served ... *my chance*!

I don't say a word
I don't start anything – just go for it:
"Be back in a bit".
Helmet snapped on, trainers laced up in no time
and I take out my new beauty

and I RIDE

I feel the wind's constant breath tighten the pores of
my skin. It is the opposite feeling from a warm bath.
Just now feels like a day ago.
So here I am, pedalling, grinning
It could be any day,
I could be any age (I'm feeling about five),
It wouldn't bother me if the sun shimmered or if rain
poured (puddles to slosh in!)

It was a perfect moment, a me-experience.
I was all I could feel – *me* against the handlebars,
me upon the seat, *my* energy pushing against the
pedals – the bike felt like an extension of my body.

No other.

There I am, high off the ground *l-life's a breeze* when
you are riding a bike on a Sunday eve
– it feels like I am flying.

Blank Slate

I feel odd, light, unaffected. My mind is quieter and I feel stronger. Is it because I have decided not to please people anymore

'I am nothing' –
I kept saying that
all morning.

I'm not sure what to
do with myself.

There is a difference
between leaving and
being left. The latter
forces a reality upon
you – to look Fact in
the eye. Honesty
becomes imperative
to find the answers to
your own questions.
I am not crying. I am
not distraught. I feel
at peace, though a
little confused. I feel
the need to sit quietly
for an answer.

My confidence rises.
And a feeling of love
too ... I don't know
why, or who it's for.
I don't care what you
think of me or say to

me, I have stopped
trying to do things
to be loved back.
To have *proof* that
I'm good enough.

Looking at my baby
pictures that sit on my
dresser, I see people
holding me, cuddling
me, so proud of me
for no other reason
than because I am!

I yearn for that.

I am a clean, blank
slate. I go back to
the beginning. I don't
need to achieve.
I don't need to force.
Or criticise. Or justify.
Only flow with each
day. And live.
Oh God that sounds
so good doesn't it!
To flow ...
So harmonious,
ease-ey, gentle.

And 'live'! Ah it
sounds like breath!
The freshest cleanest
newest air just birthed
from the universe.
Live!
It is an upward force,
I can feel it.
Flow!
Sounds like a river.
Up and out, together
they make a fountain.

I want to find out
what it means
To Live.
To Flow.
To trust my inner now
it has surfaced through
stillness and honesty:
that in their eyes I may
not be good enough;
And that's ok!

Changing

Because

I am tired of

Living in a World of

Limited Infinity

Vision correction

Routine eye test before work

I couldn't have known
That the Decision To Change
Enhances one's vision –
Enables a certain
Clarity of Thought.

There is a Mind's Eye
As surely as there is a Heart's Song.

My optician told me that
The more clearly you can see something
The faster you are able to respond to it.

I wondered if he was talking about life;
And not just talking about
Wearing glasses in busy places.

I wondered if this notion of vision-correction
Was about seeing beyond
What I knew
To what was actually there.

I wondered if my eyes were as
Short-sighted as my ideas of the world.
Had I made the world smaller –
So my eyes simply reflected back this belief?
Perhaps I didn't need
To see any further than my plans.

The Decision To Change
Gives me back my Sight.

Step Two

For the first time since I knew my life to be anything
other than food, play and sleep, I was being honest
with myself.

About Me.

I was witnessing myself come to life on the page.
Here I could see myself with greater clarity than
I did in the mirror.

Or in their eyes.

*Keeping the line short to start with, begin to run
against the wind until your kite gets enough height.*

"Please knock"

Where are the boundaries between you and me
– anyone and me?

My shape, malleable; melted and modelled,
contoured by pressures I let them put on me.
Such is the heat of expectation!

I have no choice but to *thrive* in it –
Turn judgment into lessons.
Misunderstanding forces me to turn to Truth.
And I'm more beautiful for it.
Do you see now?

Thank you for helping me become beautiful.
I could have crumbled. But I didn't.

I become a diamond for withstanding it all.

So please knock,
don't make me hang a sign –
But I will if I have to.

Sorry Angry

I thought that it was wrong to feel angry with someone whom you love and who loves you just as intensely

Actually it was more
than that. I felt I didn't
have the right to be
angry towards
someone who had
dedicated their life to
raising me and giving
me all the things that
she never had.

But I *was* angry.

I didn't
Let myself
Go there.

Didn't want to
acknowledge that
dense energy; instead
I kept trying to get rid
of it thinking that I was
doing something bad.
Bad because it would
upset her if she knew
that I was angry.
It was the opposite
of what I attempted
to do each day –
make her smile.

From an early age
I swallowed my anger
and denied this basic
expression to myself;
sucked it up along
with the milk in my
bottle and alphabetti
spaghetti pasta loops
and melted cheese on
toast. And it was fine.
Because the smile
ratings were
consistently high.

As I grew older it
became harder to
suck it up. I would get
angry, be sad, mutter
frustrated words
under my breath
as I retreated to my
bedroom, away, to
avoid confrontation.
When I shut the door
I would push the
feelings down like
stuffing plasticine into
a jar. Or make them
evaporate in heavy

sighs because they
were bad. I didn't
allow myself to feel
them – that would
be dangerous, that
would be taking sides
– against the person
who gave me life.

Her heart must be
aching. But it's not my
fault. If only everyone
else would try. Try to
keep the smile rating
high then it would
take some pressure
off of me.

It then became
a battle against
Guilt.

I felt bad
for being human,
having these emotions.

She had never said
it was okay.

No one had said that
it was okay.

I felt a crack inside.
And it hurt a lot.
Fresh tears birthed
with a sting in my
eyes. I deserved to
have feelings and feel
them and express
them. Without being
expected not to react.
Not to raise my voice.

Always the
good one.

In The Moment

Losing myself
in and around
Piccadilly Circus. Feel
–s-o disconnecte-d;
from, them.
Fine. But!

Feel disconnected
from—my-se-l-f too.

A distancing from self;
consequence of
self-critique taken
too deep?

I don't belong
anywhere in this here
and now. Far

from home; not totally
settled at work
                ... does anyone
...
                get me?

I would love to sit
comfortably in *this* seat
and *my* skin. Sink
right in Knowing that I
am fine as I am, so that
I don't need to think;
just Be and Float.

Blur around the edges,
turn down the sounds.
Fade people in and out
as I choose; you see –
I don't wanna fade ...
or ... be ... faded ...
because I know how
that feels.

Been there every now
and then.

But this time I want to
be Here. Be Here.
Now. Be Here And
Now.

And be *MORE THAN
okay* as I am. As I am.
As. I am ... what?

Oh uh ummm.
Don't really like it.
This. It. This. Thing.
Feeling. Sticky air
darting eyes – f-f-ffind
something. Find
something to catch my
attention. *Make* it –
interesting. – Oh look!
A man cutting down a
tree. Oh! *Phew!* Out of
the cloud of nothing.

My Reflection
I've been living life through everyone else's eyes

Do you know what I see
when I peer at myself in the mirror?

I recognise my reflection
As someone else's perception
Without a context
I lose all sensation
I just want to find me
Invite revelation.

So I'm starting a Journey
I'm yearning
To learn
About a person
That I call I –
What is she like?
Unlike?
Does she have a
Secret that makes her
Come to Life?

Other Peoples' Standards

I'm starting to see how limiting it is to apply
other peoples' standards to my world

A single moment can expose you.

And everything you thought that you knew.
The moment when the rest of your life will be
determined by a decision that you must make.
Do you know how to choose?

Who taught you about "best" "know" and "right"?
What happens if I accept their definitions of "should"
"wrong" "good"?

It matters, when your heart is on the line and pulls
away from your mind.

If you do not choose you live with a perception that
may not truly be yours. It is the lack of your Own
which betrays you in That Moment.

And I can tell you that in That Moment there is no
time to think; the time to debate and wonder is Now.
So when That Moment comes you *know* what you
need to do to keep your world in balance.

– Suddenly my taste buds change. My tongue migrates in
an instant to another food climate – between spoonfuls ...
– it is an almost-out-of-body experience. I don't know what
is happening ... it feels like ... rejecting ... – cannot stomach
the same dinners – I can wait forever for the next episode –
realising – I don't want this anymore –

This is where the crumbling starts –
when Familiar becomes
such a weightless burden
that you wonder
if Easy isn't worth it any longer ...

You feel Altered;
And they will say that you have changed.
But you haven't,
You've just woken up.

After a long sleep you can feel a little disorientated.
But that won't stop you from opening your eyes
Will it?!
No!
Oh no!

Waking up
Is the best Beginning in the history of Your Time.

Dear Sang

I'm sorry Sang,

I never allowed you to make mistakes.

So I didn't let you be, explore ... live, feel fully.

I didn't trust myself.

I couldn't trust myself because I lived in my head.
I wouldn't go anywhere near the edges – just in case –
I'd fall. And no one would help me – save me – in case no
one would – love me.

It was like holding tight to a child's hand while walking
through town. Squeezing when she spots the balloon man
and surges towards him, gripping as she runs to chase
blown-bubbles. Because ... something might happen –
in that moment – of – freedom. Unplanned, uncontrolled
bursts of feeling.

I suppressed it. That spontaneity. That curiosity.
I'm sorry.

I've learned now to open my hands to the world.
To offer the emptiness of my palms as prayer.
To have faith in the inevitable infinity of life –
and its possibilities.

x x

Hope

Alone can be beautiful
And beautiful can be kind
And kind can be lost
And lost can be found.

*If I have Faith
does it mean I should not cry?*

*I just want someone to know how I feel.
But I am afraid to explain*

I have never said it out aloud
– not fully, clearly, intentionally. Accurately.

I don't know which words to use to describe ... this.

And without the right words then they will not get it;
Might avert their faces toward the ceiling thinking:
That must be hard!
– Or confess:
'I can't imagine!'

They're right, they can't imagine.
Because even if I *could* find the exact words and
pieced together a faithful translation they might still
swirl the coffee around in their cup, not-quite look at
me and say
'I can't imagine!' – because it is so surreal.
I'm sure it would not make any sense in their world.
They wouldn't understand why it's such a big deal.

But it's a part of Who I Am – and that changes the
axis on which my world spins.
If I have faith does that mean
I should not cry?
Am I supposed to wait with an unbreakable smile?

> (Because I *know* in the long-run
> it will be worthwhile
>   ... but *still* ...)

Am I allowed to feel tired of waiting? Be angry?
Would anybody listen if I ask the clichéd questions
Why me?
Why would you let me cry? (whispering *if You love me)*

I feel so *bad;* – I know it's for a reason, I know
I should be *grateful,* but ...

I just. Feel. Pain
I need a shoulder to cry – on but no one is in range.

> So I sit on my bed scribbling sense.
> Trying to get it out,
> as if it's trapped in
> the pen. Moving so
> fast, leaking out
> almost-coherent ink.
> *Get it out* – so it stops inside my head.

> I feel like if I tell – try to explain – I will seem
> as though I am complaining about a God that
> they think doesn't exist. I'd just be doing their
> lack of faith justice.

> It's almost hypocritical – I choose to take
> His Word, yet can't bear the silence of
> the journey.

I scratched too hard and made a patch in my
eyebrows. I did not care the moment I scratched –
perhaps two seconds ago – but I care *now.*
And everyone will notice.
Damn.
I almost can't be bothered to care again.
What's the point in looking beautiful
If my heart is aching from balancing.

In this Moment

*I feel like I don't need anything
or anyone else. The Experience*

is deep. I forget where I am, almost.
Connect with the meaning.
Float on the notes.
Get lost within the vibration.

Become the notes I play and sing
with no sensation of body.

Alone
Playing the piano in my house
Singing words of expression
Whilst everyone is out.

No one is listening but me.

It is not for anyone.

It just is.
For me.
By me.
The world through *my* eyes.

I begin to process differently.
Something magical is taking place.
I am in it.
I am of it.

Today I realise there is more to me than
meets the eye; and that I can give to myself
as a friend and lover.

My Life

'Life'

Takes on a new meaning

Now that it's

Mine

I'm Normal
A workday evening

It's normal to feel
anxious
It's normal to feel
anxious

The bath helped; and
my book took me into
another world.
Now the book lies face
down on the wicker
wash basket and here
I am. The plug lies on
the sidebar like a
lifeless fish.
The bathwater draws
away from me in
constant bubbly swirls;
I want to go with it.
`

*I was always afraid of
the dark water-flumes
at the pool.*

I step out of
desperate thoughts
and dry myself.

It's okay to be scared.
It's normal.

It's okay to be anxious.
It's normal.

Lift left leg – drop leg
onto wicker basket –
towel – dry: up down
up down – leg down.
Foot meets floor,
head spins.

I lose the floor for a
very real second – but
catch myself. Right leg
up onto the wicker
basket. I dry it slowly
this time. Up, down,
up, down, with more
care because I need
to watch out for
myself. I know how
I get when I'm anxious
– when this happens –
when it comes –

I tell myself that what
I am feeling is totally
normal. And that *I* am
normal. That this is all
so very, very normal.

Both feet firmly on
the ground now.
Breathe.
Repeat:
I am normal.

Both feet firmly on
the ground now.
(I can't feel them
mind you)

The fear is so real
(that *I* am suddenly ...
not –) but I cannot
lose control.

Do you hear me –
I cannot lose control!

I look at myself in the
mirror. Repeat: I am
normal. I look at the
reflection of my body
and see a body.
I don't hear the beauty
pageant. I don't try
to spot where I could
tone up, I don't pay
attention as to whether
I'm symmetrical today.
I just wonder:

Why haven't I done
it before?
Why have I never let
myself be okay as I am?
Be on my own side?
Help myself?
Just let myself
be human?
And try to find some,
anything to smile about!

Feel scared shitless and
not try to fight it?
Just be it; because
in this situation it is
almost impossible to be
anything else.

Why hadn't I realised, or
even considered, that it
may be possible to relax
into fear - if fear is my
honest truth right now?

All the while recalling
(the way I did when I
learnt my timestables)
that I Am Normal.

Pick 'n' Mix

Days start and end the same
Sitting tight in a weary train
People do not talk or laugh, it doesn't seem right –
We are blessed with freedom, blessed with life
Only to forget what it means.

Remember how, as kids
Life felt sweeter with treats
Nothing mattered
When striped paper bags were in *our* grasp
Because *we* had the power today! Hooray!

Carefully sampling magic delights
Fingers wonder nimble and light
Trying to decide without taking a bite
How did it make me so happy?

On the walk to work I spot window treats
Stroll in and pretend to be
One of the gang, as I grab a bag
And begin to fill it with sweets.

Suddenly I've gone back in time
Lost 5 foot, I'm only 9
Cola bottle skies, cherry cube seas
Consume me

Until:
I hear not coins – but sweets
Bouncing at my feet!
I'm dancing with the colours of the rainbow!

Scene change:
My grown-up clocks the mess I've made
Peeks to see who's turned this way
I quickly end this stupid game
And hand over twenty-four queen heads.

And I make it through a working day
Without a sneak peep or taste,
Finally! I'm sitting down
In the same old train, with the same old crowd

I pull sour faces from fizzy fish,
Giggle and bite on chewy sticks
Keep on going despite the stares –
I thought you're too busy to care?

By the time the clock strikes eight
I slip off my heels and paperweight
I feel happily sick and there's no one to say
'I said so'!

Check emails, mobile, then my tongue!
(It's green!) Don't wanna brush my teeth!
I need to save that taste I found
(Because I think It's me!!)

As pillows meet a swooning head
I believe again;
Drifting into sleep
My inner child comes with me.

I trapped Myself through Them
Letting go of concern which consumes, frees me

I want to let go.

But I'm scared that
they won't be okay.
I am protecting them

From what?
From what Sang?

From themselves ...
from each other ...
from their definition
of reality ...
from their version
of life.

Today I was *so*
frustrated, *so* mad,
so *uuuurrrgghhhh*.
They were not *listening*
to what I was *saying* –
I felt like *I* was going
to explode! *Me*!
For *them*! *Why should*
I bottthhheeerrr!!!

I suddenly became
aware of how much
it *affected* me.

Now I have no choice
but to let go

As I let go of being
responsible for protecting
them I set myself free –
I let go of that concern
which consumes –

Stop worrying about
them and I can focus
on me guilt free!
Without feeling selfish.
Guilt free! I stop
holding them back and
keeping track. I let go
of more than three and
I feel myself releasing
me – in a way – from
expectations of what
they want to see, what
they think of me.

They just become
them;
And I become me.

We become equals:
equally imperfect,
equally untamed,
equally capable.

I see now that
I trapped myself
through them.

Cutting string that
I lovingly wove
around their wrists
and I feel it slacken
on my own also.
It's the law of gravity.

I let them go
I let them be. *Breathe*

What do Thoughts look like?

What does it mean to
'think for yourself'?

What is that *like*?

I mean our thoughts –
are they *really*
our own?

Are *my* thoughts
completely *mine*?

Who put them in my
head? (I swear I can
hear familiar tones
prompting, nudging,
whispering to me
and through me while
I try to decide).

But the actual thought:
How did it form?
How was it
conceived?
Am I simply the
midwife?

My mother needed
someone to drive to
Heathrow Airport to
pick up my aunt who
was coming to visit
from abroad.

When she asked
which one of us could
go – my brother or me
– he jumped up and
I stayed silent.

Why?
Why did the idea of
driving to a new place
excite him and cause
me to hesitate?

A thought. Nothing
more. A thought that
I would not be able ...
But I hold a licence!
I passed my driving
test! With fewer
minors than
my brother!

Okay, I am not great
at geography.
My sense of direction
is, well, questionable.
And yes, I do get lost a
fair amount.
But I am careful!
It's true that I don't
like hill-starts. And
giant multi-lane
roundabouts do freak
me out sometimes.

But what prevents me
picking up my aunt?
What if there was no
one else to collect her
but me?

People drive to new
places everyday.
They *have* to.
They would be
limited if they stuck
only to the roads
that they knew.
They wouldn't get far.
Never see new places.
Eventually perhaps
feel trapped ...

So what
am I *really* thinking?

Or does it not matter
what thoughts come?

I have an Inkling of
a deeper thought
within me. Which
isn't a thought at all,
but a knowing. And
that knowing tells me
that Thoughts are not
always the Truth.

I find Myself here

This I know for sure:

that Music soothes
that Words clarify
that Expression is a form of Truth

And even if no one ever reads this *I know* how *I* feel
about it all. And God can read these words as well
as my heart.

Out of my head and onto a page where I can step
back from myself. Be honest with my Self – have
a conversation with my Self.

I can tell if I am telling a lie, or trying to – because
my fingers stumble and hesitate the same way my
tongue would.

I cross out dishonest words when I re-read myself,
sometimes with pride and sometimes with shame,
sometimes with denial and other times with a hapless
sigh because I wish ...

Seeing words in black and white, in a true form,
means I cannot hide from what is on that page – it is
either true or false. And false word = delete button.

Smile Dependent

I don't have to smile
Because no one's happiness depends on it.

Picture me: chirpy and cheerful as a sunbeam with
those around me sat sombre, like big boring rocks.
I would turn my beam towards them; if it did not
work I would put on sunglasses.

But I cannot do it anymore!
I cannot take responsibility for your smile!
I'd be pretending; taking from you what is yours.

Today, it got to the point where I would not, could
not smile. It was too hard to accomplish.
So I simply stopped trying.
I was reluctantly self-concerned.
And you got over it after a while.

... You don't need me like that ...

I feel a huge weight lift. I'm saying huge.

I can feel thoughts tumble and cartwheel in the
space created in my brain. Like I have cleaned my
hard drive.

You see, I kept tabs on what made your face light up
when sunshine itself could not, when bluebirds
chirping outside did not reach your ears – let alone
your lips ... It was tiring.

... And now you are free to smile as you please.
And so am I ... ☺

I'm afraid of the Power I have to make Myself Happy
I think I've found It; or rather It found me

I cannot change
anyone's life. I do
not have that power.

Sometimes I feel guilty
about all of the good
things that I have.
I think *How come
I got away? Why me?*
I don't know.

I don't think
Why not me? when
I see the super-rich
and the super-lucky.

Both states of mind
are perceptions of
inequality and my
relation to it, together
with an intrinsic sense
of injustice about the
way the world *is*.

I suppose we all have
hang-ups, things to
overcome. Hang-ups
that stop some people
from believing in God,
or in our own worth,

in *It* – because others
do not have *It* –
Oh! The audacity to
dream!! Whilst others
are dying of starvation
or survive, shelterless
or parentless or both ...

Why does wanting
more – seeking
happiness for myself –
make me ungrateful?

Suddenly I don't want
'It' anymore.

I can make do with
what I have right now.

            *... but that's a
lie – I know that ...*

And it's ironic; no one
else knows about the
decisions I am trying
to make, the dual ache
I feel when I ponder
about all the suffering
in the world and yearn
for my deepest desires.

I'm tempted to hide:
to climb into my locker
and sit there and think
(a lot), about how and
why It got here and
found *me* ... but the
locker is about two
square feet so I can't.
Plus this is an
open-plan office so
everyone would see
me get in, defeating
the point of hiding
in the first place.

So I sit at my desk, all
quiet. The papers in
front of me just don't
matter in all honesty
and by comparison.
And the office feels ...
almost inhuman the
way we are arranged,
sitting head-down
rabbiting away.

*I know why
they can't love.*

By lunchtime I am
dying to go outside
to the park and try
to figure this out – but
I have said 'no thanks'
to lunch with my team
for over a week.

I should really go
today. I walk with the
others to the canteen.
Perhaps there are no
answers; perhaps the
biggest challenge is to
accept. There is a
brand of humility in
receiving what you
feel you do not
deserve. There is no
beauty in sacrificing
yourself only to be as
miserable as those
whom you pity but
cannot reach.

I'm starting to wonder
whether courage is
really about accepting
greatness; accepting
It for yourself when
it presents to you
regardless of whether
you believe you are
ready or worthy.

It is not for you to
decide.

I want them to be Proud of Me

We all seek things
Deep within
our being.

Feelings like cravings.
It's pure need.

Today – just now –
it was approval
I needed.

Approval from my
parents – the thought
just came to me
though I suspect it
had been lurking,
shy, unsure of when
to let itself be known.

Today I wondered
whether they were as
proud of me as they
were of my siblings –
I wondered what they
thought of me – at
home, unemployed –

I've never felt the
need to wonder this;
have never questioned
whether they love me.

But I want to know
what they think of me.

This thought comes:
Do they judge me?

Then I start to think
that I can see them –
thoughts I would
rather not see them
thinking ... are they
about me?

I've caught them;
I tried to interpret
them: it's not shame,
they are not *ashamed* –
it's worse: they look
at me like they don't
understand me ...

But today Mum smiles
at me as I walk past
the living room.
It is a genuine smile.
And I feel inadequate.
I wonder why she is
smiling at me.

I – I want to say and
believe that I am
wonderful just as I am
and that is why she is
smiling at me – and it,
it might be why; but –
I feel like there is a
But.

Maybe the But is me.
I'm getting in the way.
Again. I created it all.

I want them to be
proud of me – yet
when I worked in one
of the most prestigious
institutions in my
field, their super-
proud-parent-ness
made me cringe.
Because to me the job
really wasn't all that.
To them it had all the
prestige that they
worked so hard for
to give me a chance
at claiming.

Listen: I am thankful.

But their pride didn't
mean much – not
because I didn't value
it, but because *I* wasn't
proud of it or of me. It
was because I was not
happy there. I told
them to stop "going
on" and that it wasn't
that big a deal.
Because it wasn't –
It didn't sweep me off
my feet or make me
silly-smile.

I want them to be
proud of me.

But here is the thing
that I discovered:
I want them to be
proud of the things
that *I* like and *I* want
and *I* love and *I* am
proud of myself for.

I want them to be
proud of *me*,
I know that one day
soon they will be.

I have to be patient.

I want them to be
proud of me.

And I think they are
deep down, secretly.
They just don't know
it yet.

I have Days where I do not Know the Truth anymore

It's as if I'm starting
to notice some things
and un-notice others.
I'm not being mystical
or dramatic. I find it
unnerving actually.

When I wanted to find
myself I didn't realise
that a new me would
be accompanied by a
new world.

And this new world
does not always make
much sense. I don't
know if I like it.

In this new place,
sense is jumbled up
into anagrams:
roel, tcurleu, tebs,
cuscuses, dhouls, tiem,
ubt, sppuodes.

I find out that so many
words are just used
to fit an expectation
or to create one; are
used loosely and
interpreted strictly.

And that we buy into
them – I bought into
them – on a daily basis
without questioning,
without thinking
about what they
really mean.

It is a weird sensation:
as if as I grow, my
world sort of crinkles
around me in some
places, inwards
and outwards.
I imagine it's what
seed breaking through
soil in a first shoot
experiences.
It feels disruptive.

It is seeing the old
unfold; undress itself
to reveal something
different to what you
knew it to be.

I used to feel a little
envious of some of my
friends and their life
that was so fast paced
and glamorous!

People people people!
Drama drama! –
Yet now, now it seems
like there is something
lacking when I listen.
*Isn't there something
more?* I find myself
thinking as she
recounts another
weekend over
the phone.

And that lacking
feeling – it's mine.
I feel it seeping into
lots of things:
Living in the same
town, following the
same routine, repeat,
repeat until it dawns
on me that what
I have seen is only a
tiny part of the world.

Suddenly I experience
The Panic – I need to
see, taste, and
experience the rest!
Now!
But how?

With a new
consciousness the
world expands; desire
awakened stretches
my mind further.

It pulls familiarity
apart forcing me to
deconstruct 'my', 'me'.

Yes, yes there were
tears;
And also wonder.

For a while I played
chords on a piano that
needed tuning.

I feel constricted in the
moment of realisation
– because I can't tell
if it is really for me,
you know ...

> *Things I do because
> I should. Visit
> people I don't want
> to.
> Good mornings at
> work I don't mean.
> Traditions that don't
> come with any
> explanations.
> Chirpy at the
> breakfast table
> when really my
> heart is aching and
> I'm worried sick.
> I don't want to do
> that anymore.
> I don't have to!
> I don't have to!*

Time becomes
precious as I realise
that I have things that
I want to do.
Frustration rises
quickly – at ... it's
coming to me ... I am
... frustrated at ...
feeling forced!
Limited! To – to – to
'do things' ... which
take up time: time that
I could do something
else with – oh gosh,
there *is* something
I want to do –and –
and I am not doing it!
For some reason – the
why isn't important –
I have been doing
favours that I don't
really want to be
doing. *How is that
Truthful Living?*

I see it now: observing
myself at breakfast,
I don't talk and they
ask why. I don't want
to say, because at
times you cannot
articulate the language
of the soul – it cannot
be framed into words
that say only of our
own experiences.

I don't want noise.
I need space. I don't
want people around
and I wonder when
in my day that can
happen and realise:
never –

Suddenly I can't
swallow my toast;
my throat goes dry
and it won't go down.
I reach for the teacup,
subtly I hope, and feel
an intensity spreading
... on my face in big
letters "Go Away".
And even then I don't
know who I'm talking
to – them or me.
I'm not upset.
I just ... can't breathe.
I contemplate not
going into work –
to just go elsewhere ...
But of course I don't.
I don't know how to
do that ... I choke on
sandpaper toast,
gagged by newfound
sensations – until
I find out how:
I just Do It: –
it's the only way
to get the saliva to
start working again.

Honesty

I miss that honesty between the people closest to me.

They're acting out of fear – what they think *should*
happen, what *should* be.

Who, now, listens and responds with Humility?
Ultimate Honesty? With an open heart and mind?

If Truth were Respected – I would be able to Express,
say *anything*; but I worry:

What if my words are fobbed off or misunderstood?

They don't accept the truth – or the possibility of
another truth – my truth – and so it feels like –
on some level – they are not accepting me either.

What is really on our minds?
What do they actually want to say?
Maybe they don't even know their own truth
So how can they see mine?

Breakthrough

And when I focus on
me (and not on them),
when I am doing what
I enjoy, I feel a glow
inside, like love.
And it stays within.
It is for me. I feel a
flush in my cheeks.
I am in love with me.
I feel the first signs.
I sense a connection
to my self. Ooh!
Oh a connection!
Aha! It's something
you can actually feel!

Carrying My Own Destiny

I want to be able to say that
I am living my best life. Passionately.

How do I know that I am doing that?
How can I *tell* when I am creating my best life?
Am I at the point where I can say that
I am doing that?

How long does it take? What does it involve?
I've dreamed it so many times – but it gets stuck
in my throat – and – I – choke –
on the images that stay inside me
– not anymore!

I want to hold my life in my hands.
Cup freedom, cherish it as best I can.
Know where it is.

To remind myself that it is up to me and no one else –
that each and every day it is *up to me*.
So that I can go forward in grateful leaps and bounds.

With God's Grace,
I wish to carry My Own Destiny.

The air in the House after an argument

is like post-flame smoke, but without the smell.

Clear, but duller. Air moves slower as it becomes
thickened by emotion and uncomfortable words
that were thrown out like angry fists.
It has the same effect just it's on a different plane.

Intention hovers, misinterpreted, silently finding
the correct words to make it right, thoughts of how
to take it back without losing pride – even though we
are family. Perhaps this fact makes it harder because
we can't just walk away from each other. Love that
connects at that deeper level is elastic that holds us
together whilst we try to pull apart.

The air shifts marginally when you walk through
the room, barely detects the slight turn of a head that
looks out of the window, away, or as he reaches for
the remote control to drown out the silence.

Let My Hair Down Secret
The soundtrack changes

I whack on Beyoncé's 'Best thing I never had'.

Listening, I want to be free and vibrant and expresss.
Confidence wrapped in a melody that makes me
walk taller. Act bolder. Forces me to admit that
I want to be beautiful.

It's not that the song *makes* me like that – it simply
uncovers something that is already there – that part
of me that lives just under the surface.
The music is a trigger, a signal to come out.

I live vicariously through the song; the blending of
notes amongst voices coaxing a deep desire from
within me. I come to serve myself; I could not have
done it without help.

Oh! It's too much fun, dance and move to it, sing
with it – I fling my hair and roll my head side to side.
My body has an energy –
I call it The Empowered Woman.

And best of all, no one saw!
It wasn't directed at anyone.
It had no purpose, yet I feel different after.
My state is altered.

When I go down for dinner no one knows.
No one *needs* to know – it's *my* secret.

Sunshine on a Pavement Slab

... Do I look super crazy grinning like a tomcat on a train packed with sleepy commuters bored-faced and forced to read the Metro ...?

I almost feel *bad* for feeling this happy.

It's as if my face could pop from this amazing feeling – of *believing* in the *possibility* ...

I'm sucking my cheeks in restraint – though it looks like I am pouting – *un*sexy. I am actually just chewing on my smile. Pursing my lips could be another option – though this has the drawback of lips that inevitably tremble until the smile breaks through again.

I'm giving myself shivers.
Like a pavement slab warmed by sunrays that drift along its breadth – *mmm* that four o'clock sun.

I feel gentle waves of Love.
Self-tenderness.

I feel the Crumbling

I can actually feel
the crumbling.

Bones crushing at
th –the– b-bo-bottom
of m-my ribcage.

Each diminution takes
some breath away.
Don't *hear* crunching;
feel debris piercing
soft skin – from the
inside out.

Commuters just see a
pretty face waiting for
the 07:56 train to
London Waterloo.
Headphones plugged-
in listening to someone
else's life, someone
else's version of 'I Am'.

I can relate – a kinship
forms. *Sympathy* – for
myself too. *Yes, yes* –
singing about the same
heartache. The notes
rise towards the roof
of my mind in
gentle vibrations.

Need to sing it out,
before any more ribs
are sucked into the
black hole swirling
inside, giving me
funny-tummy as
I step onto the train.

I Dare Myself

Beautiful Responsibility

The most Beautiful thing about taking Responsibility
is that
You have the power to control your Response to life.

It's about Choice.
And it puts you right in front of the steering wheel.
All you need to do is hold your hands out to meet the
circle that knows no start, no end, no right, no wrong.

It moves with You.

Step Three

I started to delve deeper. I brought God into the picture. And Truth. And Love. And Dreams. Hope and Happiness – I pursued Ideas that seemed less relevant to 'adult life', less tangible in the 'real world'. I needed to Know for myself whether I could be someone Greater.

And it was a beautiful combat, an infusion of rain and sunlight at every juncture.

As your kite gains altitude, let the line back out. Watch it soar.

A Moment within a Moment

I start and end my day with a cup of tea
English breakfast in the morning and
Afternoon blend for the beginning
Of the eve of the day –
They serve the same comforting purpose
Are twin faces of the same friend.

I try not to get addicted to
The taste warmth comfort and smoothness, the
knockmebackforamillimillisecond aroma, the
grounding, settling into self,
the sensation of home though you are nowhere near.
To the way it takes the edge off.

Tea brings me back to myself
(as Twinings rightly say).
I yearn to wake up to and sleep with myself
So I make time for tea. And it's so easy!

I love to drink in big, long, gulps
That thwack emotion;
Subtle tastes and rich essence
Stretch my breath into Bhujangasana.

Tea is always appropriate. Always.
We are eternally allowed
To dip into thoughts and soak,
Warm our body to receive,
Guide peace towards us.
We are entitled to take a moment
To have a Moment
For ourselves.

How can I trust myself?

If I am not connected with that Part of Me –
That deep, deep portion of Myself –
How then can I trust the thoughts that surface?

If I have Learned anything

No, I don't expect your
world to stop or start
according to mine.

If I have learned
anything it is that
you will not feel my
pain because it is
only ever mine.

That you can never
fully understand
because you cannot be
my truth – the mixture
of all my memories,
beliefs, subconscious
meanderings that *I* am
not even aware of.

That you can love me
but still not be there
for me (you have your
own breath, too).

That we cannot
save the ones we
love from the pain
of their own journey.

That it's important
to know what I can
rely on to prompt
my smile.

That I can cry and yet
be okay, knowing that
part of me naturally
wants to go on – else
I would fall with my
tears. I am stronger
than I thought I was.

That I only need to
know what *I* think of
myself – *truly*, and see
only *that* in the mirror.

That I do not answer
to anyone – not even
my mind.

That when I try my
best I hold my head up
even if tears run down.

That I am beautiful
because I say so.
Because I still love,
and because I exist
on the inside too.

That I won't just give
up; I will just love me
harder. Because no
one can know what
I need in *this* moment
better than I do.

Detour after Work
Turkish tea, marble cake and Me

It has been such an intense day – in a great way.
So much happened that I feel as if I am in the final
minutes of a quick-spin machine wash.
I need to break the cycle.

Although I left work early enough to get the fast
train, I find myself slowing down as I approach the
bridge that leads to the station; I sense myself being
drawn to the deli. I give in.

Push. Ding! Pick a seat.

Shoes slide off. Feet up and tucked under my
bottom. It's Turkish tea, marble cake, and Me.
I melt into my surroundings. There is nothing to
experience but peace of mind and bodily comfort.

Sometimes I need exactly this – a moment that
enriches my day. It's funny: I met new people today
– and a few months ago I would have gone home
feeling good about myself because they appeared to
like me and respect me – yet today, nowadays, I am
seeking something more for myself. I gave Inkling
the benefit of the doubt when some feeling inside me
said it wanted to Pause. I feel so right sitting here.
I look out of the window; in this state I feel me.
In being me, I see the River Flowing.

It is so close. What a view. I am grateful for it.
Though I usually do not have much appreciation
for the grey landscape, today I can easily convince
myself that I am in a café somewhere in Amsterdam

or Paris, between mouthfuls of marble cake and sips
of Turkish tea, with the blend of Arabic music and
olive trees.

I achieve nothing in this moment.
I think of nothing, solve nothing, and learn nothing.
Look at and notice nothing.
Express nothing (except ordering more tea).
Deliberate nothing.
I listen to nothing spoken – only instruments,
I allow the hubbub in.
Yet there is a quality about this moment, which
makes me think that these moments are what life
is about.

I don't know how to describe these minutes of
existence; it is like standing because I can and
because something inside me wants to.

Do I feel more real in this moment? I am not sure.
I know that this moment is deeply fulfilling.
Deeply necessary.

I've found a new sanctuary. It's not like any coffee
shop; there's something about this place. Now that
I have found me here once I know that I can find me
here again and again. Feel me here over and over.
The only thing I would want now, as I run my hands
through my hair, are gentle hands massaging my
shoulders, and a kiss.

I would be happy to stay here for a few hours ... but it
is time to go; the train only runs every hour.
Precious moments can be created too.

Now I know.

A Note to Myself

Face it: you are not their favourite person but that's okay.
You are My favourite person ☺ I see all the wonderful
things that you do and are and strive for.

I believe in you ...

But, you could let your hair down a little – love things
that you can't change about you, they give you your
personality – I mean – just stop trying to be perfect Sang.

I'll love you every single moment of every single day
because I know that you are a precious soul always
remembering to add beauty to your world, always trying
to compose peace and harmony into the backdrop of life.

Today, though, I ask that you forget trying to do anything.
Instead, just be. Please – I would love you more for it,
you would love you more for it. And I will get to see the
real you that is kept tucked away. I just want you to come
out and play! Play! Laugh! Love! Live! As much as
you can! Loving – is intuition more than an act.

What matters is that you give yourself the freedom you
know that you need and deserve. You will never stop
loving others – so don't worry. It's part of what makes
you wonderful. Loving. It's inbuilt in you. So you can
afford to let go a little.

Your constant,

Sang

I Overcame the Day

I got the better of the day.

It was a struggle this evening. Invisible walls came in.
I was afraid. Couldn't feel a way out:

> *– tomorrow – the same as today – seems impossible –*
> > *but do-able.*

> > > *Now I can breathe.*

I do not regret that I had a day such as this
I am grateful I made it through:

I sat with Mum and Dad and ate home cooked food
I cried on the phone to my sweetheart
I opened up my laptop and wrote.

The day did not beat me.   I got through.

I go to bed in peace and exhaustion.   *I won.*

It does not matter what passed.
What matters is that *it passed*.

I overcame myself
I overcame the world.

Giving Birth to Destiny's Child

I believed that my destiny lay in the hands of others; it left me at their mercy. Now I know that destiny is within me. That it exists only if I exist. It flows only if I do

Instruction: Activate Destiny Through Movement

We keep Destiny away when we stand still.
You see, it does not just happen to the chosen few,
nor work on you; Destiny works *through* you.
It sounds so good.

Lesson one: Destiny Works Through Me.

The Oxford Dictionary defines 'destiny' as
"... the power that predetermines the *course*
of events." 'Course' is defined as "... an onward
movement in time or space. 4. a route or direction
taken."

In other words: Destiny Is Active Not Passive.

It makes sense. It is only once we start to move that
Destiny can guide us. If we hide under the bedcovers
of life how can we expect to know daylight? The one
light that may blind at first, gives sight purpose.

Realisation: The Doors Were Never Closed, I was.

Possibility does not just happen. Opportunity cannot manipulate you. You have to meet in the middle – it comes towards you, you come together. It's like finding a life partner or making a new friend. They don't pop up out of thin air and attach themselves to you. You have to do something. You have to give yourself a chance.

Lesson two: Destiny Needs A Date.

Give change a chance by taking charge and Become the force in your Own Life.

Say it with me: I Am The Momentum!

Dear God

Give me the humility to find myself
– not by searching for others, or through others
thinking that I know better.

Give me the courage to be myself.
Let my breath be constant in the face of strong winds
and opinions.

Let me relax so that my muscles melt into a steady body ...
Into Your arms as mine own.

Give me the wisdom to let go so that I may go
Wherever I please in this moment and in those to come.

Give me love to keep my days bright and worthwhile –
So that
The close of the day is only a later sunrise
in different shades.

Let me own thankful eyes and gracious feet
For each day I traverse on this earth and in consciousness.

Give me faith of mind so that mirrors reaffirm
and never doubt,
So that reflections teach, yet do not show all.

Let me feel a moment – of peace –

Please Lord:
This is my prayer:
Please.

Breathe

If it's all I do today
If it's all I achieve today
If it's all I can maintain
I will have mastered
Something
So simple
So profound
So sacrosanct
So taken for granted

Maybe I would be loving myself
(Whatever that actually means).

Normality and Rough Patches

Sometimes I forget that the celebrities I admire do the
same everyday things us normal folk do. They wake
up in the morning and go to the bathroom (and it
doesn't smell of roses either), they take time to eat,
open a bank account and experience the spectrum of
emotions that we do. They walk, talk, burp and
laugh, cry, have fears and desires. Yes, they do.

The difference, then, is that they do all of these things
with a certain Grace and Elegance.

I believe that Grace is associated with living your
passion – you carry it with you, as oneness with life:

He knows the choices that he has made, the sacrifices,
the bliss. He knows that *he* made the choices.

She knows a thing or two about the journey; this is
the Elegance in her laughter. Love and security spur
confidence and develop posture. Self-worth gives
permission to speak slowly – I notice that she takes
her time to choose the most exact words, to honour
and savour that word-choice. I see wisdom in the
way she settles into the arm chair and tucks a strand
of hair behind her ears – there is magic in her
movements, I swear.

Fighting for your dreams bestows a sense of
entitlement and courage that isn't necessarily painted
with colours of ego.

So I remind myself as I crunch cornflakes
and shave my armpits that I am Experiencing Life!

I imagine being the person I want to be but am afraid
to be and practise in those small insignificant actions.

I tell myself that life is beautiful! That I am loved!
And somehow it feeds into my actions and my body
and my posture. I pretend that I am already 'there' –
and I get a tingle of excitement (I am actually starting
to believe myself!).

Then something or other kicks off.
I ask God why can't we all just get along?

We can't be afraid of the rough patches

It's sunny outside but heavy clouds loom in here.
And I sit fighting anger with cultivated high spirits –
like a delicate Chinese fan trying to settle flames
around me. I end up a little worse for wear, a little
sooted-out.

And I reach a point: if I cannot get off the ride, the
only thing to do is take it as it comes by seeing it for
what it is – part of life. This is my life at the moment.

And we can hope to improve
– that's always on the table.

So I go back upstairs, pull open my wardrobe doors
in desperation and a desire not to be so; I change my
outfit, scrub off the lip gloss and opt for Vaseline
instead. I replay the last song in the CD player; read
a poem through glassy eyes and vow to do whatever
it takes to get myself back to that ... place.
(I was happy there; hope could reach me).
I touch the face that smiles at me from the mirrored
wall with my fingertips and inhale: *How did you do it?*

A Thought about Freedom

Perhaps freedom is one step at a time
One moment at a time.

As I think this I feel the light of the moon on my face.
It is soothing. I acknowledge it.

Insight

It's a split second thing!
Your body reacts
Like you've been dropped
From the height
Your soul flies
Light
Elevated
Balmy
The world freezes
And you feel a tepid flush;
Do not hear chatter
Because you've gone inside
Within, without realis-ing.

Float away from yourself but closer at the same time
Like the back-pull of a pendulum dragging one way
as it heads to the other.

It is the moment before free-fall
The plunge from mind to heart
The suspension between each breath.
All feels calm as
Caesurae of the ocean rushing in and out.
There is a pause – and in it
Pulses warmed rich nectar called Insight.

Calamine on a rash, it cools;
Thaws numbness without sensation
But with awareness
Of a deeper place within its own place.
Like flipping your belly button inside out –
If you can, that is –
Not everyone can do it.

The Truth has Nothing to Prove

Like a pearl within the
closed clam I wake up
in my mind.

I know that it is
morning because
my brain tells me so
and my body feels
rested. I do not move,
so guilty sleepiness
trickles in. I can still
get up if I choose to,
if I have to, if I want to.
But I don't want to,
so my eyes remain
resting like hands
folded in prayer with
lips parted as if ending
that same prayer.

I just be: I absorb the
moment; I experience
myself on my bed.
I sense the softness of
the pillow under my
head and my head soft
against the pillow.
I enjoy it so much that
I turn the other cheek.
Swelling waves rush
onto the shores of my
ears in a rustle, shush
and tender crunch.

I turn my cheek again
and the blanket stirs
with me.

When my body has
found a comfy spot,
all goes silent: sifted
flour settling in the
bowl type of silent.

I breathe in morning
air and the night air
tumbles over and out.

Exhalation prompts
sleep to lift itself from
me; I don't have to
push it away because
I am late, nor do
I clutch at it for as
long as I possibly can.

Because. Today I can
afford to let it take
its time.

Because. I have a
secret: I am *happy* to
be awake.

Because. This is a day
that I can look forward
to living.

A day filled with
glorious fresh foods;
taking a shower as my
nose wanders through
English gardens; I get
to write – engaging my
heart and intellect, and
be me as I please.
Mmm ... I choose.

Choice –
it feels like a luxury.

I don't know how
I didn't see it before,
take it. Well, I *know*
why, but I don't know
why. – It takes ... guts,
to look at all the
options and decide
what I want, eliminate
what I don't want.

And to do that with
any degree of certainty
I have got to be able to
see. See with a
different kind of
prescription to the
one I am used to.

Because:
It will stay under
wraps until I call
for it (voicelessly
or out loud).

And until then it will
be who or what
I want it to be; it will
even let me call it
reality if I decide to.
It can be pushed into
a lie – it *lets* me! It lets
me because it's *my* job
to uncover it –

The Truth
has nothing to prove.

And it seems like a
never-ending journey.

Warm feet meet
cold floorboards
preparing for My First
Conscious Step.

Rock Star for Six Seconds

I feel expression under
my skin wanting to
push out.

Wait at the station.

Emotions are here too.

I don't know what to sing
(a sign of being off centre and far from my heart).

I start with a simple hum; turn the volume down
when people pass by ... And then this happens:
A fast train passes through the station without
stopping and a chorus launches from my lips:

'I am riding high,
I don't wanna come down,
hope my wings don't fail me now'

It brings a smile to my face,
I bring a smile to my face.

And it is so ... precious!

Those few seconds.

I am trying to Think

Am I still
Even if I stand still
And the world moves around me
Under me
And over me
And inside me
Can I ever be still?

Was I made to be so?

Sunshine and News Headlines

The sun sits pink in
the sky this morning.
On this first day of
Spring I step out of
the house and little
buds are the first
things to catch my eye.
I hurriedly apply my
make-up on the way
to the station.

I rush into the ticket
office because it is
freezing, so freezing
cold this morning ...
*Should have bought
that bobble hat ...*
I walk straight to the
radiator and plonk
my bag down to zip
up my bomber jacket.
As I do, I sip on the
scene at the ticket
office; my eyes catch
the newspaper
headlines:
'Girl 14 Mauled
by 5 Dogs'.

I look at a photograph
on the page and
wonder if that is the
child referred to in the

article. I reread the
headline while soft
shades of warm
marshmallow melt
through the window
'Girl 14 Mauled
by 5 Dogs.'
That probably is her.

I pause and consider
how horrific it is.
Yellowy sunlight
flashes bravely off
the metal newsstand
and windowpanes
making me smile even
though I am cringing
from imagining what
that would ... be like.

She looks so
vulnerable in the
picture – who could
allow that? – the sun
is so beautiful.

Suddenly I feel anger
towards the sun – how
can you still shine and
rise and glow so
breathtakingly in the
face of such brutal
happenings?

How can you beam so
brilliantly despite all
the sadness?

It just
doesn't make sense.

Is the beauty of the
sun supposed to make
me feel better about
life and all the things
that happen in the
world? Does it still
rise, despite, because
that is what Beauty is?
– Hope, indestructible
even in the face
of tragedy?

I am grateful the
instant I consider the
alternative:

I imagine that the sun
has emotions like you
and I do – that it reacts
to the world – and
I see a dull grey
furnace, barely
bothering to show
on most days and
struggling to shine
on other days, rarely
allowing itself to
function because the
headlines sucked.

I decide to take a leaf
out of the sun's book
and smile with it.

I decide to be grateful
for all of the little
beauties in life.

I say a prayer for the
child and hope that
we learn as a society.

I turn my back to the
newsstand in peace,
and walk onto the
platform with joy in
my heart. Without
feeling bad.

To the contrary,
I am assured that
beauty exists
amongst and above
the worst tragedies
and human follies.

Sadness around
us doesn't mean
we stop shining.
No.
Keep shining.

Knowing What's Right
I do not pretend to know

I have enough humility to realise that This World
is beyond my comprehension. Though this does
not mean that I should try not to grasp it and seek
a Deeper Truth within it.

Do I know *anything*?
Is there anything that I can say is 'right'
with absolute conviction?
Or can I only say that in my heart I believe it to be so?

Here's what I think: that
'Right' is a journey, a measurement, an exploration,
not a destination.

So why do so many of us act
as if we are superhuman?

What would I tell my grandchildren about the
meaning of life?
I cannot answer you now for my future self.

Because Right changes as we do and stands for
something else – something that we are seeking,
a feeling of certainty *without anyone telling you or
reassuring you*.

Mathematics consists of labels, symbols and
paradigms existing within context.
It cannot show me what I desire most.

Just like you cannot tell me what makes me happy.

Your logic does not help me;
No sense of right or wrong will move me.
Only I can move myself – from the inside.

For me, I wonder whether Right means Love?
Intuitive? Not so much to do with my mind but
a deeper part of me?

What I won't do anymore is mistake Right for Truth,
and for a guarantee of love. A nod from a person
whose mind can be changed is dangerous.

It's better to come to your own understanding,
and make 'Right' a matter for your heart to decide
for you and only you.

Raw Sounds

Whenever I watch her live performances
I am mesmerised by her face as she sings.
I remember thinking 'perhaps that's her spirit
dancing across her skin'. I thought she looked
like the moon's half-sister. I remember I got a
feeling like déjà-vu. Inside, I longed for that
same release

I am weary when we get home. Mum and I went shopping but came back with naught. I have that feeling – you know the one – where you feel like you just wasted four hours and a car park ticket! Usually I am quite good at dusting off hindsight rip-off advice that makes me feel bad. But today it is sort of right (not about the car park ticket nor anything to do with time); the whole trip to town, the act of going shopping, didn't *do* anything for me.

I am agitated.

I decide (as I usually do when I feel tired or melancholy or if I have thoughts to banish or a mood to change or if I am just bored) to take a hot relaxing shower.

Standing in the bathtub with hot water streaming over me, I shiver. When I try to sing I can't. I feel totally disempowered. I sense my body contract despite the forgiving droplets. My Dreams feel so far away – unrealistic and unreachable. Stupid!

Water continues to pour itself onto my skin selflessly.

The tiredness is tamed
by the crystal spray
but my Heart feels
heavy. Then I make a
noise, like "aaaahhh".
I don't intend the
sound, don't create it
or push it out, don't
sing it or engage my
diaphragm, none of
that. It happens.

All I do is *let*
this echo *come*
from an innermost
part of myself.

It has a cave man
resonance. It is a cave
woman utterance. It is
how an ache would
describe itself, desire
leaking – not from my
mouth though.
The sound vibrates
out of each pore of my
naked body. It isn't
womanly or beautiful
or polished, but it feels
good. So good.
Effortless to create yet
it takes all my focus to
continue, to hold onto
that expression and
draw it out. I don't
want to think.

I don't wish to *be*
elsewhere. It soothes.
Quells. Purges me.
I go from "aaaahh" to
a song, *her* song 'Girl
on Fire'. Low tones.
I become attracted to
myself, to the sound
I am making. I want to
sustain it for as long
as possible.

The hot water has run
out now. I hop out of
the bathtub and dry
myself quickly rubbing
goose bumps away.
I hang my towel on the
heater – then I start to
cry – out of the steamy
blue. From the place
that The Sound lived.
I sob eternally for two
minutes. With blurry
eyes I send a text
message to Nina to say
that I love her for
teaching me how to
sing. Because I do.
I am humbled by this
power, this force.

And I know. I just
know: It is part of who
I am. It is one of the
strongest parts of me.

Gracious Air

Gracious air follows
the grace of people.

The opposite is also
true too. We may
dapple the air with a
fragrance of goodness
or pollute it with a
stinking attitude.
We subconsciously
disfigure and enhance
our outer image
rendering mirrors
tellers of half-truths
and make-up
without guarantee.

Gracious air follows
the grace of people.
Because we wear
feelings like perfume.

I catch my reflection in
a shop window and
am momentarily
startled by the lift in
my cheekbones which
catch the light and
dance with it; the way
the corners of my
mouth are broadened,
lips seem fuller, parted
ever so slightly in

Readiness.
Contentedness.
As if I'm about to smile
As if I just *know* that
something is going to
happen to make me
smile any minute now.
I can feel it.

My eyes are sparkling
... they love life!
They are so welcoming
– to myself. As I walk
along the high street or
step off the train, as
I order a chai latte
people stare.
I get it now.

They *notice* something
going on inside. They
can see traces of hope
and joy and peace on
my person.

I have seen people
like today-me before.
My spirits lifted
whenever I spotted
them and I always
thought the same
thoughts: I want to
be near them;

I wish I could be like
that too; I want to
know what their secret
is, what makes them so
happy? – But I never
had the courage to ask.

On the days I feel
plain, tired, a touch
bored, I summon
memories of those
vibrant reflections of
Me – from shop
windows, train doors,
mirrors – and infuse
My Being with
their Confidence.

I Get Up.

To change my clothes
and brush out my hair,
to read a few pages of
a book written by one
of my all-time heroes,
to play my current
favourite music track.

There is nothing more
powerful than to *let
myself Be Inspired.
Let myself Feel Beautiful.*

I allow possibility to
have a space in my
mind and in my day.

My Best Self
I contemplate: I love who I am becoming

It's like worry
can't touch me.

Fear is just out of
reach; it seems like a
distant memory I can't
quite put my finger on.

I stand as a bud and
watch My World
bloom around who
I am and what *I* need
and love and like
.·. God I'm beautiful!

I had always assumed
it was the other way
round – that I had to
slot myself into this
giant world, take what
was offered to me.

But then I would never
have known that girl
who inspires passers-
by by passing by ...
Could I feel like this ...
every day?

It's not who I am *now*
that determines my life
path but who I can be.

Who I Can Be!
What I am capable of
if I put my mind to it,
my heart into it,
if I just let myself be.

– Like swirling my
fingers in a chocolate
fondue whilst dipping
my toes in a stream –
I can have it all!

Crazy as it sounds,
it's *possible*, right?

Instead of
feeling daunted.
Instead of
putting up with.

Instead of settling.

I balance un-fulfilment
with the idea that
I have room to grow,
space to fill.
Something to work
towards and for.

So I keep moving;
I want to be the cause
and the consequence.

09:03

It is still early for me, although it is bright outside.
Something of me feels sleepy, dreamy.

> I love sunshine in the morning;
> The way see-through streaks of yellow spill
> into my room between careless curtain folds.

I love sunshine in the morning
But I crave the dawn sky.

There is something about the dawn. It is where my
soul is right now
– the Dawn.

Epilogue

The end of the Beginning.

Both feet have taken their first steps.

I am coming to the fore.

By giving Life a chance
I allow Myself
to experience Miracles I had read about
and dreamt about
but shied away from
because I did not know how.

Standing firmly in Myself
I choose a Life that I truly want.

And Live it as Me.

Aisirikutuwa Ikirikoto.

Rearranging my life.

Day by day
Slot in as much of what I Love as I possibly can
(including sleepy naps if that's what I fancy).

Eventually Living will be Loving.

Aisirikutuwa Ikirikoto: it means 'to love is to live'.

Acknowledgments

I thank my parents for the foundations they built
from which I dared to follow my dream of writing.

Thanks to Bijou Doré for a beautiful cover design.
Thank you to Malcolm Johnson for his hand in
shaping the manuscript.

My gratitude to all those who believed in me from
the beginning and supported me along the way –
you each know who you are.

I am most grateful for the encouragement that spoke
to me from the works of the late Maya Angelou.
Likewise the inspirational music of Alicia Keys
and the writings of Paulo Coelho, which gave me
the courage to share my writing with the World.

A big Thank You to Rabbit, my Editor.

References

Instructions to kite-flying are taken from information found at
www.laughingkidslearn.com
and
www.gombergkites.com.

The excerpt that appears in the Prologue is taken from an interview between Oprah Winfrey and Maya Angelou in May 2013. This is featured on Oprah's website at
http://www.oprah.com/omagazine/Maya-Angelou-Interviewed-by-Oprah-in-2013.

About the Author

Sang Ji is a writer and poet based in
London, England.

She writes for the Joy of it
and seeks to harness the power of words
to affirm, heal, liberate and transform our existence
in a World that changes in the blink of an eye.

Sang Ji's poetry and upcoming works can be found
at www.sangsnotebook.com.

Kite Envy
I Want To Be Free
is her first publication.

For copies of this book please contact
Opera on Sarovar Press
at operasarovarpress@gmail.com.